THE STUDY OF MAN

THE
STUDY OF MAN

by
MICHAEL POLANYI

THE UNIVERSITY OF CHICAGO PRESS

The Lindsay Memorial Lectures

given at the University College of North Staffordshire

1958

THE UNIVERSITY OF CHICAGO PRESS, CHICAGO 60637

To
J. H. OLDHAM

CONTENTS

7

PREFACE

THESE Lectures were intended to form an extension of the enquiry undertaken in my recently published volume on *Personal Knowledge*. But since it proved impossible to proceed from the point reached in that book without first recapitulating the relevant parts of its argument, the first two lectures had to be used largely for this purpose. The whole series can accordingly be read as an introduction to *Personal Knowledge*.

I hope that the bearing of these talks on the philosophic and educational work of Lord Lindsay will be apparent throughout. A special reference to the idea of a university, as manifested in the founding by Lord Lindsay of the University College of North Staffordshire, will be found at the end of the series.

LECTURE ONE

Understanding Ourselves

MAN'S capacity to think is his most outstanding attribute. Whoever speaks of man will therefore have to speak at some stage of human knowledge. This is a troublesome prospect. For the task seems to be without end: as soon as we had completed one such study, our subject matter would have been extended by this very achievement. We should have now to study the study that we had just completed, since it, too, would be a work of man. And so we should have to go on reflecting ever again on our last reflections, in an endless and futile endeavour to comprise completely the works of man.

This difficulty may appear far-fetched, but it is, in fact, profoundly characteristic both of the nature of man and of the nature of human knowledge. Man must try for ever to discover knowledge that will stand up by itself, objectively, but the moment he reflects on his own knowledge he catches himself red-handed in the act of upholding his knowledge. He finds himself asserting it to be true, and this asserting and believing is an action which makes an addition to the world on which his knowledge bears. So every time we acquire knowledge we enlarge the world, the world of man, by something that is not yet incorporated in the object of the knowledge we hold, and in this sense a comprehensive knowledge of man must appear impossible.

The significance which I attribute to this logical oddity will become apparent in the solution suggested for it. Its solution seems to lie in the fact that human knowledge is of two kinds. What is usually described as knowledge, as set out in written words or maps, or mathematical formulae, is only one kind of knowledge; while unformulated knowledge, such as we have of something we are in the act of doing, is another form of knowledge. If we call the first kind explicit knowledge, and the second, tacit knowledge, we may say that *we always know tacitly that we are holding our explicit knowledge to be true.* If, therefore, we are satisfied to hold a part of our knowledge tacitly, the vain pursuit of reflecting ever again on our own reflections no longer arises. The question is whether we *can* be satisfied with this. Tacit knowing appears to be a doing of our own, lacking the public, objective, character of explicit knowledge. It may appear therefore to lack the essential quality of knowledge.

This objection cannot be lightly overruled; but I believe it to be mistaken. I deny that any participation of the knower in the shaping of knowledge must invalidate knowledge, though I admit that it impairs its objectivity.

Tonight I shall try to transmit this conviction to you or at least to familiarize you with this view—for all I have to say may not convince you—by showing that tacit knowing is in fact the dominant principle of all knowledge, and that its rejection would, therefore, automatically involve the rejection of any knowledge whatever. I shall begin by demonstrating that the personal contribution by which the knower shapes his own knowledge manifestly predominates both at the *lowest levels* of knowing and in the *loftiest achievements* of the human intelligence; after which I shall extend my demonstration to the *intermediate zone* forming the bulk of human knowledge, where the decisive role of the tacit coefficient is not so easily recognizable.

I shall speak therefore first of the most primitive forms of human knowing, at which we arrive by descending to those forms of intelligence which man shares with the animals: the kind of intelligence that is situated behind the barrier of language. Animals have no speech, and all the towering superiority of man over the animals is due almost entirely to man's gift of speech. Babies and infants up to the age of eighteen months or so are mentally not much superior to chimpanzees of the same age; only when they start learning to speak do they rapidly out-distance and leave far behind their simian contemporaries. Even adults show no distinctly greater intelligence than animals so long as their minds work unaided by language. In the absence of linguistic clues man sees things, hears things, feels things, moves about, explores his surroundings and gets to know his way about, very much as animals do.

In order to bring out the logical characteristics of such tacit knowledge we must compare it with the articulate knowledge possessed by man. We see then in the first place that, obviously, the kind of knowledge which we share with the animals is incomparably poorer than that of an educated man, or indeed of any normally brought up human being. But while this richness of explicit knowledge is admittedly related to its distinctive logical characteristics, it is not itself a logical property. The essential *logical* difference between the two kinds of knowledge lies in the fact that we can critically reflect on something explicitly stated, in a way in which we cannot reflect on our tacit awareness of an experience.

To make this difference apparent, let me compare an instance of tacit knowledge with a knowledge of the *same subject* given in explicit form. I have mentioned that men can look round and explore their surroundings tacitly and that this propensity is also well developed in animals. It is known from studies of rats running a maze. A great connoisseur of rat behaviour, E. C. Tolman, has written that a rat gets to know its way about a maze as if it had acquired a mental map of it. And observations on human subjects suggest that a man, however intelligent, is no better at maze-running than a rat, unless assisted by notes, whether these are remembered verbally or sketched out in a drawing. But of course a man *can* make such notes or have them made for him. He may be provided with a detailed map of a region through which he is passing. The advantage of a map is obvious, both for the information which it conveys and for the more important reason that it is much easier to trace an itinerary on a map than to plan it without a map. But there is also a new risk involved in travelling by a map: namely that the map may be mistaken. And this is where critical reflection comes in. The peculiar risk that we take in relying on any explicitly formulated knowledge is matched by a peculiar opportunity offered by explicit knowledge for reflecting on it critically. We can check the information embodied in a map, for example, by reading it at some place that we can directly survey and compare the map with the landmarks in front of us.

Such critical examination of the map is possible for two reasons. First, because a map is a thing external to us and not something we are ourselves doing or shaping, and second, because even though it is merely an external object, it can yet speak to us. It tells us something to which we can listen. It does that equally, whether we have drawn up the map ourselves or bought it in a shop, but for the moment it is the former case that we are interested in, namely when the map is in fact a statement of our own. In reading such an utterance we are playing back to ourselves something we have said before so that we may listen to it in a critical manner. A critical process of this kind may go on for hours and indeed for weeks and months. I may go through the manuscript of a whole book and examine the same text sentence by sentence any number of times.

Obviously, nothing quite like this can take place on the pre-articulate level. I can test the kind of mental map I possess of a familiar region only in action, that is, by actually using it as my guide. If I then lose my way, I can correct my ideas accordingly. There is no other way of improving inarticulate knowledge. I can see a thing only in one way at a time, and if I am doubtful of what I see, all I can do is to look again and perhaps see things differently then. Inarticulate intelligence can only grope its way by plunging from one view of

16

things into another. Knowledge acquired and held in this manner may therefore be called *a-critical*.

We can enlarge and greatly deepen this contrast between tacit and articulate knowledge by extending it to the way in which knowledge is acquired. Remember how a map is drawn up by triangulation. Starting from a set of systematically collected observations, we proceed according to strict rules applied to these data. Only explicitly formulated knowledge can be thus derived from specifiable premisses according to clear rules of inference. And it is the most important function of critical thought to test such explicit processes of inference, by rehearsing their chain of reasoning in search of some weak link.

The contrast between the two domains should now be sharp enough. Pre-verbal knowledge appears as a small lighted area surrounded by immense darknesses, a small patch illuminated by accepting a-critically the unreasoned conclusions of our senses; while man's articulate knowledge represents a panorama of the whole universe, established under the control of critical reflection.

But if this is so, can it still be true that it is the tacit personal component which predominates in all human thought? Surely, one cannot but accept then the preference which has urged the human mind to overcome its pre-verbal dumbness and to unfold a great public

17

record of articulate knowledge. And it seems almost inevitable then, further, to accept as our ideal the establishment of a completely precise and strictly logical representation of knowledge, and to look upon any personal participation in our scientific account of the universe as a residual flaw which should be completely eliminated in due course.

And yet this exalted valuation of strictly formalized thought is self-contradictory. It is true that the traveller, equipped with a detailed map of a region across which he plans his itinerary, enjoys a striking intellectual superiority over the explorer who first enters a new region—yet the explorer's fumbling progress is a much finer achievement than the well-briefed traveller's journey. Even if we admitted that an exact knowledge of the universe is our supreme mental possession it would still follow that man's most distinguished act of thought consists in *producing* such knowledge; the human mind is at its greatest when it brings hitherto unchartered domains under its control. Such operations renew the existing articulate framework. Hence they cannot be performed within this framework but have to rely (to this extent) on the kind of plunging reorientation which we share with the animals. Fundamental novelty can be discovered only by the same tacit powers which rats use in learning a maze.

It is of course impossible to compare exactly the

level of tacit performances involved in the works of
human genius, with the feats of animals or infants. But
we may recall the case of Clever Hans, the horse whose
powers of observation far exceeded those of a whole
array of scientific investigators. They believed the
animal was solving problems set out on a blackboard
in front of it, while it was actually taking its clues for
correct answers by watching the involuntary gestures
made by the scientists themselves in expectation of
these answers. Remember also how readily and how
well children learn to read and write, compared with
hitherto illiterate adults. There is enough evidence
here to suggest that the highest tacit powers of an adult
may not exceed, and perhaps actually fall short of those
of an animal or an infant, so that the adult's incomparably greater performances are to be ascribed predominantly to his superior cultural equipment. Genius
seems to consist in the power of applying the originality of youth to the experience of maturity.

But can we go even further now and show, as I
promised, that everywhere—at all mental levels—it is
not the functions of articulate logical operations, but
the tacit powers of the mind that are decisive? I believe
we can. But we have first to reconsider these tacit
powers and define them more precisely. I have spoken
of the capacity to see things in one way rather than
another, and described also how we get to know our

way about a neighbourhood; I have said that our tacit powers achieve these results by reorganizing our experience so as to gain intellectual control over it. There is one word which covers all these operations. They all consist in comprehending experience, i.e. in making sense of it; the word which covers them all is simply '*understanding*'.

I shall dwell for a moment on this term—'understanding'. For I must not smuggle in unnoticed this apparently harmless, but in fact sharply controversial word. A powerful movement of critical thought has been at work to eliminate any quest for an understanding that carries with it the metaphysical implications of a groping for reality behind a screen of appearances. Natural science has been taught to regard itself as a mere description of experience: a description which can be said to explain the facts of nature only in so far as it represents individual events as instances of general features. And since such representation of the facts is supposed to be guided merely by an urge to simplify our account of them, rival explanations are professed to be merely competing descriptions between which we choose the most convenient. Modern science disclaims any intention of understanding the hidden nature of things; its philosophy condemns any such endeavour as vague, misleading and altogether unscientific.

But I refuse to heed this warning. I agree that the process of understanding leads beyond—indeed far beyond—what a strict empiricism regards as the domain of legitimate knowledge; but I reject such an empiricism. If consistently applied, it would discredit any knowledge whatever and it can be upheld only by allowing it to remain inconsistent. It is permitted this inconsistency because its ruthless mutilation of human experience lends it such a high reputation for scientific severity, that its prestige overrides the defectiveness of its own foundations. Our acknowledgment of understanding as a valid form of knowing will go a long way towards liberating our minds from this violent and inefficient despotism.

Meanwhile, let us go back to the subject which gave rise to this digression on the metaphysical aspects of understanding. I had shown that purely tacit operations of the mind are processes of understanding; I will go further now by suggesting that the understanding of words and other symbols is also a tacit process. Words can convey information, a series of algebraic symbols can constitute a mathematical deduction, a map can set out the topography of a region; but neither words nor symbols nor maps can be said to communicate an understanding of themselves. Though such statements will be made in a form which best induces an understanding of their message, the sender of

21

the message will always have to rely for the comprehension of his message on the intelligence of the person addressed. Only by virtue of this act of comprehension, of this tacit contribution of his own, can the receiving person be said to acquire knowledge when he is presented with a statement.

This holds, of course, also at the point from which a statement is issued. We utter a statement with the intention of saying something. Though this intention may not include an anticipation of all that will be said —since a message may develop further as it is put into words—we always know approximately what we mean to say a little before we say it. This is true even for purely mechanical computations, on which we blindly rely for uttering a statement; for we know in advance what we are doing, in trusting such an operation to speak on our behalf.

I have now expanded the function of understanding into that of knowing what we *intend*, what we *mean*, or what we *do*. To this we may add now that nothing that is said, written or printed, can ever mean anything in itself: for it is only a *person* who utters something— or who listens to it or reads it—who can mean something *by* it. All these semantic functions are the tacit operations of a person. And this holds, more particularly, of the bearing that descriptive utterances have on the things they designate. Remember how the bearing of a map on a part of the country through which it is guiding us is derived from map-reading; and how map-reading is used, conversely, to test the correctness of a map by confronting it with the facts to which it refers. This shows that the understanding of a descriptive statement must include both the capacity to relate it correctly to its subject-matter and the understanding of the subject-matter itself in terms of the statement in question.

Admittedly, if you take such statements as 'The book is on the table', which philosophers particularly like to quote as an example, the whole process of understanding what is being said and what it is being said about, as well as the relation between the two, may appear trivial. But there are vast domains of human knowledge for which this is manifestly not true. The facts of biology and medicine, for example, can be recognised as a rule only by experts possessing both special skill for examining the objects in question and a special connoisseurship for identifying particular specimens. The exercise of such an art is a tacit feat of intelligence which cannot ever be fully specified in terms of explicit rules. We shall presently see how this fact will suggest a broad expansion of the powers of human comprehension.

But let me pause here for a moment; are we not going too fast? I have said that the immense intellectual superiority of men over animals is due almost entirely to man's gift of speech. But if the powers of tacit knowing predominate altogether in the domain of explicitly formulated knowledge, can we still credit our capacity to use language with such tremendous intellectual advantages? A full answer to this question would have to explain the entire range of specifically human intelligence; it can be given here only in the briefest outline.

Language offers, of course, the obvious advantage of verbal communication. We profit by information received at second hand, and more particularly by the communications of the dead, transmitted cumulatively from one generation to the next. This has been often pointed out. But articulation does not merely make us better informed: it enriches us even more by increasing our mental power over any given piece of information. I have mentioned how easy it is to trace itineraries on a map. This exemplifies the great speculative advantage achieved by storing up knowledge in a handy, condensed form. Maps, graphs, books, formulae, etc., offer wonderful opportunities for reorganizing our knowledge from ever new points of view. And this reorganization is itself, as a rule, a tacit performance, similar to that by which we gain intellectual control over our surroundings at the pre-verbal level, and akin therefore also to the process of creative reorganization by which new discoveries are made.

So we can explain after all the tremendous intellectual advantage of articulation, without in the least derogating from the supremacy of man's tacit powers. Though the intellectual superiority of man over the animal remains due to his use of symbols, this utilization itself—the accumulation, the pondering and reconsideration of various subject matters in terms of the symbols designating them—is now seen to be a tacit, a-critical process. It is a performance, like understanding or meaning something, which can be done only in our heads and not by operating with signs on paper. Our whole articulate equipment turns out to be merely a tool-box, a supremely effective instrument for deploying our inarticulate faculties. And we need not hesitate then to conclude that the tacit personal co-efficient of knowledge predominates also in the domain of explicit knowledge and represents therefore at all levels man's ultimate faculty for acquiring and holding knowledge.

We may face then at last effectively the problem raised in opening this lecture by the a-critical character of tacit knowledge. We have seen that when we understand or mean something, when we reorganize our understanding or when we confront a statement with the facts to which it refers, we exercise our tacit powers in search of a better intellectual control of the matter in hand. We seek to clarify, verify or lend precision to something said or experienced. We move away from a position that is felt to be somewhat problematic to another position which we find more satisfying. *And this is how we eventually come to hold a piece of knowledge to be true.* Here is the tacit doing of our own of which I spoke at the beginning, the unavoidable act of personal participation in our explicit knowledge of things: an act of which we can be aware merely in an unreflecting manner. And this situation appears now no longer as a logical oddity. For we have seen that the kind of tacit powers by which we commit ourselves to any particular statement operate in various elaborate forms throughout the realm of human knowledge, and that it is this personal coefficient alone which endows our explicit statements with meaning and conviction. All human knowledge is now seen to be shaped and sustained by the inarticulate mental faculties which we share with the animals.

This view entails a decisive change in our ideal of knowledge. The participation of the knower in shaping his knowledge, which had hitherto been tolerated only as a flaw—a shortcoming to be eliminated from perfect knowledge—is now recognized as the true guide and master of our cognitive powers. We acknowledge now that our powers of knowing operate widely without causing us to utter any explicit statements; and that

even when they do issue in an utterance, this is used merely as an instrument for enlarging the range of the tacit powers that originated it. The ideal of a knowledge embodied in strictly impersonal statements now appears self-contradictory, meaningless, a fit subject for ridicule. We must learn to accept as our ideal a knowledge that is manifestly personal.

Such a position is obviously difficult; for we seem to define here as knowledge something that we could determine at will, as we think fit. I have wrestled with this objection in a volume entitled *Personal Knowledge*. There I have argued that personal knowledge is fully determined, provided that it is pursued with unwavering universal intent. I have expounded the belief that the capacity of our minds to make contact with reality and the intellectual passion which impels us towards this contact will always suffice so to guide our personal judgment that it will achieve the full measure of truth that lies within the scope of our particular calling.

*   *   *

These brief hints must stand here in place of many pages. Accordingly, I shall now take it for granted that we accept personal knowledge as valid and shall proceed to develop the structure of such knowledge further in the direction which will lead us into the field of the humanities. This opens a great prospect. For I

hope thus to comprise within a single continuously variable conception of knowing, both the process of acquiring such knowledge as is comprised by natural sciences and the knowledge of man himself as the seat of all knowledge; and I hope that this conception will readily expand even further to a comprehension of man as the source of moral judgment and of all other cultural judgments by which man participates in the life of society. Though my survey will have to be sketchy, I think that it will clearly suggest a perspective within which the essential unity of these aspects of man can be revealed.

The structure of tacit knowing is manifested most clearly in the act of understanding. It is a process of *comprehending*: a grasping of disjointed parts into a comprehensive whole. The characteristic features of this process have been carefully traced by the psychology of gestalt in the course of the last forty years. Yet that enquiry has missed an aspect of its subject which I believe to be decisive for our understanding of knowledge and for our corresponding appreciation of man's position in the universe. Psychologists have described our perception of gestalt as a passive experience, without envisaging that it represents a method—and indeed the most general method—for acquiring knowledge. They were probably unwilling to recognize that knowledge was shaped by the knower's personal action.

But this does not hold for us. Having realized that personal participation predominates both in the area of tacit and explicit knowledge, we are ready to transpose the findings of Gestalt-psychology into a theory of knowledge: a theory based primarily on the analysis of comprehension. Let me outline this theory here briefly.

We cannot comprehend a whole without seeing its parts, but we can see the parts without comprehending the whole. Thus we may advance from a knowledge of the parts to the understanding of the whole. This comprehension may be effortless or difficult, indeed, so difficult that its achievement will represent a discovery. Yet we shall acknowledge the same comprehending faculty at work in all cases. Once comprehension is achieved, we are not likely to lose sight again of the whole; yet comprehension is not completely irreversible. By looking very closely at the several parts of a whole, we may succeed in diverting our attention from the whole and even lose sight of it altogether.

These psychological observations can be transposed now into the elements of a theory of knowledge. We may say that when we comprehend a particular set of items as parts of a whole, the focus of our attention is shifted from the hitherto uncomprehended particulars to the understanding of their joint meaning. This shift of attention does not make us lose sight of the particulars, since one can see a whole only by seeing its parts, *but it changes altogether the manner in which we are aware of the particulars. We become aware of them now in terms of the whole on which we have fixed our attention.* I shall call this a *subsidiary awareness* of the particulars, by contrast to a *focal awareness* which would fix attention on the particulars in themselves, and not as parts of a whole. I shall also speak correspondingly of a *subsidiary* knowledge of such items, as distinct from a *focal* knowledge of the same items.

Let me illustrate this distinction between subsidiary and focal knowledge and show at the same time how it transcends the distinction between tacit and explicit knowledge. Take words, graphs, maps and symbols in general. They are never objects of our attention in themselves, but pointers towards the things they mean. If you shift your attention from the meaning of a symbol to the symbol as an object viewed in itself, you destroy its meaning. Repeat the word 'table' twenty times over and it becomes a mere empty sound. Symbols can serve as instruments of meaning only by being known subsidiarily while fixing our focal attention on their meaning. And this is true similarly of tools, machines, probes, optical instruments. Their meaning lies in their purpose; they are not tools, machines, etc., when observed as objects in themselves, but only when viewed subsidiarily by focusing attention on their purpose. The skilful use of a tennis racket can be paralysed by watching our racket instead of attending to the ball and the court in front of us.

This brings out an essential point. We use instruments as an extension of our hands and they may serve also as an extension of our senses. We assimilate them to our body by pouring ourselves into them. And we must realize then also that our own body has a special place in the universe: we never attend to our body as an object in itself. Our body is always in use as the basic instrument of our intellectual and practical control over our surroundings. Hence in all our waking hours we are subsidiarily aware of our body within our focal knowledge of our surroundings. And, of course, our body is more than a mere instrument. *To be aware of our body in terms of the things we know and do, is to feel alive. This awareness is an essential part of our existence as sensuous active persons.*

We can recognize this existential character also in other forms of subsidiary awareness. Every time we assimilate a tool to our body our identity undergoes some change; our person expands into new modes of being. I have shown before that the whole realm of human intelligence is grounded on the use of language. We can reformulate this now by saying that all mental life by which we surpass the animals is evoked in us as we assimilate the articulate framework of our culture.

The vast accumulation of explicit statements of fact in our modern culture fosters an equally extensive proliferation of thought in control of facts. Subsidiary awareness is a dwelling of our mind within the subject of which we are subsidiarily aware, and an articulate framework is therefore accepted ultimately as a happy home for our understanding; it is the soil on which our understanding can live and grow, while satisfying ever further its craving for clarity and coherence.

My illustrations of the distinction between subsidiary and focal awareness have covered both the domain of tacit and explicit knowledge. This reflects the fact that all kinds of rational knowing involve an existential participation of the knower in the subsidiary particulars known by him as their joint meaning or purpose. Only a totally isolated and completely meaningless thing could be brought fully into the focus of our attention, but even in this case we should be subsidiarily aware of our own bodily adjustments in terms of the localization ascribed to the object in question.

We have seen how comprehension can be destroyed altogether by shifting attention from its focus to its subsidiary particulars. It is not surprising, therefore, that we may often apprehend wholes without ever having focally attended to their particulars. In such cases we are actually ignorant, or perhaps more precisely speaking, *focally ignorant* of these particulars; we know them only subsidiarily in terms of what they jointly mean, but cannot tell what they are in themselves. Practical skills and practical experience contain much more information than people possessing this expert knowledge can ever tell. Particulars that are not known focally are unspecifiable, and there are vast domains of knowledge, relating to living things, the particulars of which are largely unspecifiable. The human physiognomy is one such thing. We know a face without being able to tell, except quite vaguely, by what particulars we recognize it. And this is also how the mind of man is known. A man's mind can be known *only comprehensively, by dwelling within the unspecifiable particulars of its external manifestations*.

This conception of the mind, based on our theory of comprehension, will allow us to attribute to the mind of another person the same faculties of comprehension which we use in comprehending it. For the unspecifiable external manifestations of this mind, in which we dwell in comprehending it, are that mind's own dwelling place. They are the bodily actions of the person whose mind we are observing, actions of which he himself is subsidiarily aware in terms of the intellectual control he exercises over his surroundings. Indeed, we ourselves, facing the person in question, may be what he just now comprehends. He and I may be mutually

33

comprehending each other, by dwelling within one another's external mental manifestations.

We have achieved here a continuous transition from the personal knowing of things to the personal meeting and intercourse between equal minds. We may regard this as a substantial advance towards that unifying perspective of the different aspects of man, which we have set out to discover.

But I have yet to give their full weight to some features of comprehension at which I have only hinted so far. I have spoken of our *craving for understanding*, and have mentioned the intellectual passion which impels us towards making ever closer contact with reality. These passions are powerful forces pursuing high hopes. Indeed, if the shaping of knowledge is achieved by pouring ourselves into new forms of existence, the acquisition of knowledge should be found to be motivated by the deepest forces of our being. We see in fact that repeated frustrations in solving a harassing problem can destroy the problem-solver's emotional balance—even if he be an animal. As to man, we may say that his whole universe of feelings, just as his entire human intelligence, is evoked by the articulate heritage to which he is apprenticed. We know also that every increment in this educational process is induced by spontaneous acts of the growing mind. To a mind on the alert, whatever seems intelligible presents a prob-

lem and stirs it to the prospect of discovery. Thus will
the active mind avail itself of ever new opportunities
to undergo a change that will make it more satisfying
to its modified self.

Discovery, invention—these words have connota-
tions which recall what I have said before about understanding as a search for a hidden reality. One can discover only something that was already there, ready to
be discovered. The invention of machines and the like
does produce something that was not there before; but
actually, it is only the knowledge of the invention that
is new, its possibility was there before. This is no mere
play with words, nor is it meant to derogate from the
status of discovery and invention as creative acts of the
mind. I am merely referring to the important fact that
you cannot discover or invent anything unless you are
convinced that it is there, ready to be found. The
recognition of this hidden presence is in fact half the
battle: it means that you have hit on a real problem
and are asking the right questions. Even painters speak
of solving a problem, and the writer's work is a quest
following an endless succession of literary problems.
This situation is beautifully represented for sculpture
in Michelangelo's unfinished St. Matthew, now in the
Academy in Florence. We see there (as the inscription
by G. B. Niccolini points out to the students of the
Academy) how the artist is about to cut away the stone

from around the figure that he has perceived inside the marble block.

Here then is a brief hint in answer to the great question which I had set aside: namely, whether knowledge, admittedly shaped by the knower, can be determined by him as he thinks fit. A passionate search for the correct solution of a task leaves no arbitrary choice open to the seeker. He will have to guess, but he must make the utmost effort to guess right. The sense of a pre-existent task makes the shaping of knowledge a responsible act, free from subjective predilections. And it endows, by the same token, the results of such acts with a claim to universal validity. For when you believe that your discovery reveals a hidden reality, you will expect it to be recognized equally by others. To accept personal knowledge as valid is to accept such claims as justified, even though admitting the limitations imposed by the particular opportunity which enables the human mind to exercise its personal powers. This opportunity is then regarded as the person's calling—the calling which determines his responsibilities.

I have said before that I accept this situation and will not argue it here in detail. I accept therefore also that a passionate comprehension necessarily appreciates the perfection of that which it comprehends. The fact is unmistakably revealed by the emotional climax that accompanies discovery. Passions seek satisfaction and intellectual passions seek intellectual joys. The most general term for the source of this joy is beauty. The mind is attracted by beautiful problems, promising beautiful solutions; it is fascinated by the clues to a beautiful discovery and pursues untiringly the prospects of a beautiful invention. In fact, we hear beauty more often mentioned today by scientists and engineers than by critics of art and literature. Modern criticism wants to guide understanding rather than to evoke admiration. But this is merely a change of emphasis; for all understanding appreciates the intelligibility of that which it understands, and hence the internal harmonies of a complex work of art evoke our profound admiration, simply by being understood.

Yet I suppose that for some minutes past, at least since I mentioned Michelangelo's unfinished St. Matthew, you have been wondering whether I was not drifting inadvertently away from the theory of knowledge. Have I not wandered absent-mindedly across the frontier which is said to separate sharply the knowledge of facts from the appreciation of values? No, I have moved deliberately from facts to values and from science to the arts, in order to surprise you with the result; namely, that our powers of understanding control equally both these domains. This continuity was actually foreshadowed from the moment when I acknowledged intellectual passion as a proper motive of comprehension. The moment the ideal of detached knowledge was abandoned, it was inevitable that the ideal of dispassionateness should eventually follow, and that with it the supposed cleavage between dispassionate knowledge of fact and impassioned valuation of beauty should vanish.

A continuous transition from observation to valuation can actually be carried out within science itself, and indeed within the exact sciences, simply by moving from physics to applied mathematics and then further to pure mathematics. Even physics, though based on observation, relies heavily on a sense of intellectual beauty. No one who is unresponsive to such beauty can hope to make an important discovery in mathematical physics, or even to gain a proper understanding of its existing theories. In applied mathematics— for example in aerodynamics—observation is much attenuated and the mathematical interest often predominates; and when we arrive at pure mathematics, for example, number theory, observation is effaced altogether and experience is alluded to only quite dimly in the conception of integers. Pure mathematics presents us with a vast intellectual structure, built up altogether for the sake of enjoying it as a dwelling place of our understanding. It has no other purpose; whoever does not love and admire mathematics for its own internal splendours, knows nothing whatever about it.

And from here there is but a short step to the abstract arts to music. Music is a complex pattern of sounds constructed for the joy of understanding it. Music, like mathematics, dimly echoes past experience, but has no definite bearing on experience. It develops the joy of its understanding into an extensive gamut of feelings, known only to those specially gifted and educated to understand its structure intimately. Mathematics is conceptual music—music is sensuous mathematics.

And so we could go on extending our perspective, until it took in the entire range of human thought. For the whole universe of human sensibility—of our intellectual, moral, artistic, religious ideas—is evoked, in the way illustrated for music and mathematics, by dwelling within the framework of our cultural heritage. Thus our acknowledgment of understanding as a valid form of knowledge foreshadows the promised transition from the study of nature to a confrontation with man acting responsibly, under an over-arching firmament of universal ideals.

LECTURE TWO

The Calling of Man

I CLOSED my last lecture with a far-reaching promise. I said that the acknowledgment of understanding as a valid form of knowledge will allow us to study all human experience by essentially the same method. I actually sketched out a path which would lead smoothly from the exact sciences to the study of man, and even further, to a confrontation with man, engaged in responsible decisions under a firmament of universal obligations.

This is a stimulating programme; but whatever its merits, it is clearly too vast to be carried out here convincingly. I must limit myself therefore to an illustration of its more salient features. These will become apparent in the form of certain problems which we meet when trying to pursue this programme. We shall see in particular a cluster of difficulties arising around the conception of responsibility.

I have said that the shaping of knowledge by the knower can lay claim to universal validity by submitting to a strict sense of responsibility. But though this doctrine may satisfy us when applied to the domain of natural science, it meets with increasing difficulties when we pass on to the study of man acting responsibly within the bounds of his human obligations. Such studies seem to involve us in responsibilities which go far beyond those previously envisaged in recognizing the claims of a personal knowledge. For here we have to understand actions relating primarily to moral, possibly civic, or even religious obligations, and in doing so we shall exercise a judgment which is based in its turn on our own moral, civic or religious beliefs.

But can we accredit an understanding shaped by our moral and civic responsibilities? We know how such responsibilities shade into political obligations, and how these in their turn form part of the established institutional framework, or else are merely the expression of political partisanship. Are we to subscribe then to a theory of knowledge which allows the shaping of knowledge to depend on such ephemeral and parochial impulses? Surely, a judgment determined by the outcome of a struggle for power and profit cannot be accepted as authentic; at some point the acceptance of moral responsibility for the shaping of our knowledge of man will inevitably turn into an acceptance of bias, prejudice and corruption. Personal knowledge, as established by a responsible decision of the knower, degenerates here into a mere caricature of itself.

I think this shows that our conception of personal knowledge had not yet been sufficiently consolidated. We must lay down the foundations once more, in such terms that we can develop from them a conception of human responsibility not liable to be misconstrued as subservience to politics or business.

This task will appear, on reflection, to form part of a greater problem. If we are to vindicate human responsibility against the compulsions exercised by man's social setting, we shall have to establish first the existence of a human mind capable of making decisions of its own within a human body controlled by the laws of physics and chemistry. We shall have to think also of the fact that the human person which we are trying to consolidate has come into being by evolution from an inanimate universe. And, on the other hand, we shall have to face the paradox that man's decisions are regarded as reflecting the highest degree of personal judgment precisely to the extent to which they appear most rational and in this sense most impersonal. Though we may not be able to explore all these great questions here, we shall have so to shape our conception of man's dignity and obligations that these problems should not find us quite unprepared.

But before we try to build up this argument, let us go over once more and reinforce the ground on which it is to be based. The theory of Personal Knowledge offers an interpretation of meaning. It says that no meaningful knowledge can be acquired, except by an act of comprehension which consists in merging our awareness of a set of particulars into our focal awareness of their joint significance. Such an act is necessarily personal, for it assimilates the particulars in question to our bodily equipment; we are aware of them only in terms of the things we are focally observing.

We can speak then of two kinds of knowledge. To know something in the usual sense is to be focally aware of it. To be aware of something subsidiarily means that we are not aware of it in itself, but as a clue or an instrument pointing beyond itself. Such awareness may vary over all grades of consciousness, and in consequence of this the particulars of a comprehensive entity may be unspecifiable in two different senses of the term. The clues offered by processes within our body, of which we become aware in terms of things perceived outside, may be completely unconscious. An extreme case of this is our awareness of the processes taking place in our eyes when we look at something: we are aware of these only in terms of the things observed by virtue of them. In other cases we are

44

vaguely conscious of the particulars functioning as clues. We may instantly recognize a familiar writing or voice, or a person's gait, or a well-cooked omelette, while being unable to tell—except quite vaguely—by what particulars we recognize these things. The same is true of the recognition of pathological symptoms, of the diagnosis of diseases and the identification of specimens. In all these instances we learn to comprehend an entity without ever getting to know, or to know clearly, the particulars that constitute it. Here we have things composed of particulars that are *unspecifiable because they are unknown.*

But a particular pointing beyond itself may be fully visible or audible and yet be unspecifiable in the sense that if attention is directed on it focally—so that it is now known in itself—it ceases to function as a clue or a sign and loses its meaning as such. I have mentioned that by repeating a word a number of times you can reduce it to a mere sound without meaning. Similarly, our awareness of a pattern can be dissolved by concentrating our attention on its separate details in turn. *Dismemberment* of a comprehensive entity *produces incomprehension* of it and *in this sense the entity is logically unspecifiable* in terms of its particulars. Both kinds of unspecifiabilities, the stronger one, due to our ignorance of the subsidiary particulars, and the weaker one, due to the purely functional meaning of such particulars, will play their part in my argument.

I shall proceed approximately as follows. First, I shall show that the two levels of personal knowledge, that of a comprehensive entity and that of its particulars (in terms of which the entity is unspecifiable), represent *two distinct levels of reality*; and second, that there obtains between two such levels a peculiar logical relationship, derived from the distinction between subsidiary and focal awareness. Once I have established this relationship for the example of two comparatively low levels of reality, I shall proceed to erect on top of these a consecutively rising set of levels, right up to that of responsible human personhood. Within this framework it will appear possible for man to exercise a responsible choice, even though he admittedly remains rooted in lower forms of existence in which there is no room for such choices. These acts of choice will be characterized by comparing them to acts of discovery. They will be seen to exert personal initiative to the utmost by the act of submitting to the demands of their own self-set ideals. To acknowledge the reality of their freedom will appear then as equivalent to an acknowledgment of these ideals as valid. This will consolidate responsible choice in the status ascribed to it by the conception of Personal Knowledge.

*   *   *

The two levels of reality which I shall first contemplate, will both lie in the domain of the inanimate. The upper level will be composed of machines. Every kind of machine, from typewriters to motor-cars and from telephones to pendulum clocks are to be comprised here; and each of these kinds of machines will be represented by hundreds of different types, each type being present in many thousands of individual samples. As to the lower level, it will consist of the parts of machines seen in themselves as mere inanimate objects, their function as parts of a machine being entirely disregarded.

Let me show first that the upper of these two levels is in fact unspecifiable in terms of the lower. Take a watch to pieces and examine, however carefully, its separate parts in turn, and you will never come across the principles by which a watch keeps time. This may sound trivial, but is actually of decisive significance. For the study of inanimate objects constitutes the science of physics and chemistry and the study of machines forms the sciences of engineering, and we may now conclude, therefore, quite generally, that the subject-matter of engineering cannot be specified in terms of physics and chemistry. Let loose an army of physicists and chemists to analyse and describe in utmost detail an object which you want to identify as a machine, and you will find that their results can never tell you whether the object is a machine and if so, what purpose it serves and how.

The reason for this is, of course, quite simple. Textbooks of physics and chemistry do not deal with the purposes served by machines. But the science of engineering speaks at length of these purposes, such as communication, locomotion, heating, lighting, spinning, weaving and hundreds of other manufactures. Hence engineering can deal also with the way in which these purposes are achieved by the aid of machines, while physics and chemistry can form no conception of them.

But lest you may still feel that these observations are too obvious to merit serious attention, I shall recast them to make their true scope more fully apparent. Assume, for the sake of argument, that we possess a complete atomic theory of inanimate matter. We can then envisage the operations of a Universal Mind in the sense of Laplace. The initial positions and velocities of all the atoms of the world being given for one moment of time, and all the forces acting between the atoms being known, the Laplacean Mind could compute all future configurations of all atoms throughout the world, and from this result we could read off the exact physical and chemical typography of the world at any future point of time. But we now know that there is a great and varied class of objects which cannot be identified, and still less understood, by establishing their complete physical and chemical topography, for they are constructed with a view to a purpose which physics and chemistry cannot define. So it follows that the Laplacean Mind would be subject to the same limitation: it could not identify any machine nor tell us how it works. Indeed, the Laplacean Mind could identify no object or process, the meaning of which consists in serving a purpose. It would ignore therefore the existence not only of machines but also of any kind of tools, foodstuffs, houses, roads and any written records or spoken messages.

We can broaden this generalization even further by recalling that, according to the theory of Personal Knowledge, all meaning lies in the comprehension of a set of particulars in terms of a coherent entity—a comprehension which is a personal act that can never be replaced by a formal operation. It follows that a Laplacean Universal Mind would know little that means anything. For though it could admittedly advance from its knowledge of atomic configurations —by aid of the kinetic theory of matter—to some physical and chemical facts, it could never attain any knowledge of such truly meaningful objects as living beings and the things essentially related to the interests of living beings. The mathematical monster which was thought capable of reading off the future of all human endeavours from the atomic configuration of a primordially incandescent universe, appears actually restricted to a range of predictions that are of negligible interest to man. We shall find this conclusion confirmed by examining more closely the peculiar logical relation between the elements of two successive levels of reality.*

Let us go back again then to machines and define the logical relation between the two levels of knowledge that apply respectively to machines as organized wholes and to their parts as mere inanimate bodies. Machines are constructed of parts which jointly serve a given purpose by operating according to certain principles. The operational principles of machines are known to the science of engineering and unknown to physics and chemistry. But admittedly, when operational principles describe the parts of machines as organs performing certain functions in the operation of a machine, some general physical and chemical properties of the parts are presupposed thereby. The parts must be made of a suitable solid material, strong enough for its purpose and neither volatile nor readily soluble in water. No machines could be built at all in a gaseous or liquid universe. Indeed, the opera-

* Contrary to a widespread view the Laplacean predicament is not avoided if classical mechanics is replaced by quantum-mechanics. (See *Personal Knowledge*, London, 1958, p. 140 n.)

tional principles of machines rely altogether on the mechanics of solids, and may rely heavily also on other parts of physics, particularly electro-dynamics. This illustrates the general relation of operational principles to the sciences of physics and chemistry. The principles of a machine require that the parts of the machine should have certain physico-chemical properties, and these may be said, therefore, to represent *the conditions for the successful operation of the machine*.

This formulation makes it clear that the knowledge of physics and chemistry is *ancillary* to the knowledge and understanding of operational principles. If we identify the understanding of operational principles with the science of pure engineering, then pure engineering alone can tell us how to achieve certain practical successes, of which pure science knows nothing. But, on the other hand, only physics and chemistry can determine the conditions in which the operational principles of machines will in fact operate successfully; and so only the physico-chemical examination of a machine can detect the causes of possible failures, of which pure engineering again knows nothing.

But the status of these two branches of knowledge are not symmetrical; far from it. The practical identification of a machine must come first, and no amount of physical and chemical testing can replace this. Any such tests will in fact be quite meaningless unless they are guided by our anterior technical knowledge of the machine and are undertaken with a definite bearing on its supposed operations. Technology alone reveals the *true nature* of a machine by defining it in terms of its successful working, while physics and chemistry determine only the material conditions in which this success can be achieved and the shortcomings which may cause the machine to break down. The true knowledge of a machine which we have on the upper level is the understanding of a *purpose* and of the *rational means* for achieving it; while the knowledge of its physical and chemical topography is *by itself meaningless*, for it lacks any conception of purpose or achievement. It becomes meaningful only when orientated towards establishing the material conditions for the success or failure of a machine.

This completes the analysis of the simplest instance of two consecutive levels of reality. The result will prove applicable by easy generalizations to a series of ascending levels of far greater importance. The first of these is reached by including among machines the machine-like aspect of animals. The conception of animals as machines goes back to Descartes. It was extended a century later by La Mettrie to human beings and, following the invention of electronic computers and automatic self-regulating devices, it has recently been elaborated into a general theory of living functions, including the process of human thought. Though I do not accept these theories to their full extent, I admit, of course, that the animal body does function in many respects as a machine. A great number of patents could be taken out on the operational principles embodied in such organs as the heart, the lungs, or the eye, had these instruments of the body been newly invented today by an engineer. Accordingly, one should have no hesitation in generalizing all the conclusions we have reached concerning the two levels of significance in respect of machines to the machine-like operations in the body of animals.

But at this point we are faced with the curious fact that physiologists unanimously consider the machine-like operations of the body to be explicable in terms of physics and chemistry; it is only certain 'organismic' processes, of which I shall speak in a moment, that *some* physiologists would exempt from a physical-chemical interpretation. Must we then totally reject the professed basic assumptions of all scientific physiology?

I think we must. The science of physiology is actually based on quite different tacitly held assumptions and must be based on these. It seeks to establish the principles by which the healthy organism operates. These operational principles have the same structure as those of pure engineering: they analyse the joint functioning of different bodily organs in the successful achievement of certain purposes. No physical or chemical analysis of the body can ascertain by itself any of these operational principles, since the conceptions of purpose and of successfully functioning organs cannot be expressed in terms of physics or chemistry. A complete physico-chemical topography of an organism would in fact be quite meaningless. Physiology can be advanced by physico-chemical investigations only if applied to problems of physiology, and these must be formulated in terms of previously known or surmised operational principles. Physico-chemical enquiries on a living body can only seek to determine the ways in which the functions of the organism are performed and to detect the causes of any functional disturbances.

To develop the full strength of this argument and at the same time to generalize its bearing further, let me assume once more that we possess the powers of a Laplacean Mind capable of establishing the complete atomic map of any object and also of computing this map for all future points of time. Let us imagine that these powers are to be applied to a living frog. In order to do this we must first know frogs and be able to identify a particular one, and we must also be able to distinguish living frogs from dead ones. Without the anterior knowledge of these comprehensive features the Laplacean enquiry could not be started. But even so, the Laplacean information that we gained would mean little, unless we could discern from it such further comprehensive features as the existence of different organs and their respective functions, including not only their machine-like operations but also such regulative or 'organismic' processes as maturation and regeneration. But could we derive these further features from our Laplacean prediction of atomic configurations? We could do so only by discovering the corresponding physiological shapes and patterns within these configurations; and for this we should have to rely on the same faculty for identifying comprehensive entities by which the physiologist normally establishes such features from the observation of living animals.

Let me sum up this result from a slightly new angle. Living beings and processes of life are known to us by personal acts of comprehension. An observation of particulars which dissolves such a comprehension would be justified, and justified only, if it proved that the process of comprehension was deceptive and the comprehended entities non-existent. But the science of physiology assumes that living beings, their organs and the functions of these organs are real. This science must therefore always remain based on the kind of knowing which alone can establish the existence of such coherent entities. Any specification of these entities in terms of their particulars can be meaningful only if it reveals the manner in which these particulars function within these entities. Such an analysis should determine the material conditions for the successful operations of such an entity and indicate the short-comings which may impair its operations and cause them to break down.

Owing to the sketchy manner in which I have to proceed here, the term 'physiology' has been taken to include the study of all lower levels of life as conducted by the sciences of anatomy and embryology, and by descriptive botany and zoology. I shall now move on rapidly to the higher level formed by the active be-haviour of animals and men. This will clearly confront us with the existence of individuals governed by an active centre. Such a centre co-ordinates the animals' voluntary movements under the guidance of its per-ceptions for the purpose of satisfying its cravings or allaying its fears. It is the appetitive-perceptive agency within the animal. The patterns of animal behaviour governed by such centres are largely innate, but all animals, from worms upwards, can learn new habits adapted to the necessities and opportunities of new situations. This faculty, the **faculty** of learning, has been extensively studied by experimental psycholo-gists, particularly in animals, and I shall now compare the logical structure of science when operating on this level with that of science operating on the level of physiology.

Consider the study of learning. We seek here to understand a process of understanding and are thus taking for our subject-matter an activity similar to that by which our knowledge of it is being established. Suppose, for instance, that we have set to a rat the task of getting to know its way about a maze. Such knowledge is largely unspecifiable and hence the experimenter's knowledge that the rat has learned the maze is at least equally unspecifiable. At some moment we shall say that the rat's behaviour begins to show that it has grasped the topography of the maze, because its behaviour has become similar to that which we feel that, equipped with the rat's sense organs and barred from using linguistic clues, we ourselves would show if we had just begun to know our way about the maze.

We see appearing here a vivid and far-reaching application of the theory that we can know a meaning only by a subsidiary awareness of particulars which jointly constitute the meaningful entity, and that such a subsidiary awareness of particulars involves their assimilation to our bodily equipment. Applied to our learning experiment this means that we have to dwell within the unspecifiable manifestations of the rat's intelligence which we are trying to detect and to understand. This indwelling, is in fact, but a particular instance of a more general principle. Indwelling alone can make us aware of an animal's sentience. We owe therefore our entire knowledge of the appetitive and perceptive life of animals to our powers of indwelling. If an animal's sentience greatly exceeds our own, as for example in homing pigeons, we have to construe the feelings in question as a generalization of our own experience. Ultimately we always rely on the belief that animals have feelings similar to our own in so far as their bodies resemble our own.

Sentience makes new kinds of achievements possible to the animal and correspondingly offers them occasions for new kinds of failures. If physiological functions fail, this is due to disease or mutilation; sentient faculties are equally subject to such pathological disorders, but their exercise is also subject to *error*. This implies the emergence of a new feature: for by imputing to an animal the capacity to err, we presume that it is controlled by a rational centre. The appearance of such a centre clearly opens up a new level of existence, lying above the machine-like automatism or 'regulative' processes that constitute life on the lower, physiological, level. Indeed, this centre of hazardous believing and acting already prefigures the centre of true intellectual commitment in man.

The stratification of reality that is revealed here can be directly recognized by recalling that an act of comprehension invariably appreciates the coherence of that which it comprehends. This lends distinctive *values* to things belonging to levels above that of natural inanimate objects. We judge machines and the physiological operations of living beings to be either in working order or out of order, and at the level of appetitive-perceptive centres we exercise, in addition to this appraisal, the assessment of rightness and error. Both these levels of comprehension are unspecifiable in terms of physics and chemistry, since these sciences cannot appraise any kind of success or failure, but the higher of the two levels of life is also unspecifiable in terms of the lower. For in so far as organisms are represented as machines, they have no appetitive-perceptive centre; I shall say more about this relationship in a moment.

We shall ascend for this purpose by a further step of appreciation to the highest level in the hierarchy of living beings, which is our own, the level of man. Animals may be lovable, but man alone can command respect, and in this sense we humans are the top of creation. To deny this would be to repudiate the unique responsibilities which this position entails. But I want to acknowledge these responsibilities; my acceptance of Personal Knowledge forms part of this acknowledgment.

The distinctive qualities of man are developed by

education. Our native gift of speech enables us to enter on the mental life of man by assimilating our cultural heritage. We come into existence mentally, by adding to our bodily equipment an articulate framework and using it for understanding experience. Human thought grows only within language and since language can exist only in a society, all thought is rooted in society. The paleontologist and philosopher Teilhard du Chardin has called the cultural stratum within which the human mind dwells on this planet, the *noosphere*, and I support this usage.

Chimpanzees may show distinct signs of mental strain and they clearly enjoy successful ingenuity; but from these faint stirrings of a pure intelligence, man alone has developed in his noosphere a whole universe of mental passions. By contrast to his bodily passions, which man shares with the animals, the satisfaction of his mental passions does not consume or monopolize the objects which gratify it; on the contrary, the gratification of mental passions creates objects destined to gratify the same passions in others. A discovery, a work of art, or a noble act, enrich the mind of all humanity. Man, hitherto self-centred, enters thereby on a participation in timeless and ubiquitous things.

This process determines the spiritual grounds of the human mind. Let me illustrate this in a limited way by the example of science. The cultivation of science depends on the sharing of a passionate interest in a type of knowledge, bearing on a particular system, called 'science', which is acknowledged as valid by a set of mutually accredited experts and accepted on their authority also by the general public. In describing this web of scientific activities as a legitimate gratification of mental passions which lastingly enriches the mind of humanity, I implicitly accept the current standards of scientific value and the soundness of the prospects pursued collectively by current scientific enquiries. This is to accept these standards and prospects as the spiritual foundations of scientific life.

We may apply this to our whole cultural firmament, as follows.

All cultural life is based on the assumption that the standards set by our masters were right and hence the kind of truth or other mental excellence that they achieved is valid and capable of indefinite expansion. My belief in the power of human thought to discover truth in its various forms accredits therefore this power as the spiritual foundation of man's purely mental life. And these foundations prescribe the social constitution of such mental life. A man who has learned to respect the truth will feel entitled to uphold the truth against the very society which has taught him to respect it. He will indeed demand respect for himself on the grounds of his own respect for the truth, and this will be accepted, even against their own inclinations, by those who share his basic convictions. Such is the equality of men in a free society.

Mental passions are a desire for truth, or more generally, for things of intrinsic excellence. Desire for these things of the mind, pursued for their own sake, will conflict in general with desires of the body, so that the pursuit of truth will become an act of self-compulsion. And this holds also in a more essential context, namely in respect of choices taken in the exercise of personal judgment. Whether such a judgment is exercised by the enquiring scientist choosing a re-agent for the next test; or by a sculptor adjusting his chisel for the next stroke; or by a judge pondering be-tween contradictory precedents; or by a new worshipper hesitating to go down on his knees—there is always a range of discretion open in a choice. The theory of personal knowledge says that, even so, a valid choice can be made by submitting to one's own sense of re-sponsibility. Herein lies the self-compulsion by which, in the ideal case of a purely mental achievement, the utmost straining of every clue pointing towards the true solution finally imposes a particular choice upon the chooser. In view of the unspecifiability of the particulars on which such a decision will be based, it is heavily affected by the participation of the person pouring himself into these particulars and may in fact represent a major feat of his originality. Yet since this act is called forth by the agent's utmost submission to his intimations of reality, it does not abridge the universal intent of its own outcome. Such are the assumptions of human responsibility and such the spiritual foundations on which a free society is conceivable.

This definition of human responsibility sets up an ideal. Ideals are admittedly not fully realizable; but they must not be wholly impracticable. Their status is like that of 'pure engineering', which I have defined as comprising the operational principles of machines. Remember then how various misguided inventors have described machines of perpetual motion and have applied for patents to protect them, but these claims have been always rejected, for the laws of nature preclude *any* possibility for putting the principles of such a machine into operation. The problem which this lecture had set itself can accordingly be reformulated by asking: Is the ideal of a responsible choice impracticable in the same sense as a perpetuum mobile is? Does the nature of man as a material system, as a machine, as a centre of appetites, and as part of a society subject to coercion by predominant interests, permit him to make any truly independent choices?

The problem is ancient and cannot be surveyed here historically; nor is this needed, since today we have only to meet today's arguments. These are guided pre-

dominantly by the ideal of knowledge that I am reject-
ing here. Backed by a science which sternly professes
that ultimately all things in the world—including all
achievements of man from the Homeric poems to the
Critique of Pure Reason—will be somehow explained
in terms of physics and chemistry, these theories
assume that the path to reality lies invariably in representing higher things in terms of their baser particulars. This is, indeed, almost universally regarded today
as the supremely critical method, which resists the
flattering illusions cherished by men about their nobler
faculties. Our experimental psychology is dominated
by a method which aims at representing all mental
processes by a mechanical model; depth-psychology
represents human behaviour as the outcome of sub-
conscious primitive urges; and the most influential
current interpretations of politics and history assume
that public affairs are determined either by the force
of economic interests or the love of power. Here we
have before us that systematic denaturing of human
experience by modern empiricism which I denounced
in my first lecture—and now is the moment to show,
as I had promised, that the true nature of things can
be reinstated by accrediting our capacity to establish
knowledge by an act of understanding. I shall do this
by describing, within the framework of personal knowledge, the condition of man in its true relation to lower

levels of reality. But before this I have yet to clarify a little further the grounds on which we know another person's mind.

The mind is a comprehensive feature of man. It is the focus in terms of which we are subsidiarily aware of the play of a man's features, utterances and whole behaviour. A man's mind is the meaning of these workings of his mind. It is false to say, as Ryle does, that these workings *are* his mind. To say this is to commit a category mistake (to use Professor Ryle's term) of the same kind as we should commit if we said that a symbol *was* its own meaning. A comprehensive entity is something else than its particulars known focally, in themselves. Behaviourism, which suggests that these particulars should be studied in themselves, is totally impracticable. First, because the particulars, if observed in themselves, would be *meaningless*; second, because they cannot be so observed at all, since they form parts of a physiognomy and are therefore unspecifiable in the stronger sense of being *largely unknown*; and third, because it is impossible to keep track, even roughly, of a man's mental manifestations, *except by reading them as pointers to the mind from which they originate*. It is always the mind itself that we know primarily; any knowledge of its workings is derivative, vague and uncertain.

I have said that the knowledge of a comprehensive

entity is an understanding, an indwelling and an appreciation, and have indicated that these aspects of personal knowledge are closely interwoven. We can apply this now as follows. We acknowledge the sanity of another man's mind by paying respect to him. By this act of *appreciation* we enter into a *fellowship* with him and acknowledge that we share with him the same firmament of obligations. This is how we come to *understand* it and accept it that he is a person capable of responsible choices.

This conclusion, and the whole preceding analysis which leads up to it, can admittedly be affirmed only by someone who believes, as I do, in true mental achievements. To this extent my argument begs the question. But this is consistent with my purpose, which is only to show that as a result of accrediting within the framework of personal knowledge a belief in true mental achievements, we gain a view of man which confirms and strengthens this belief. It is in this sense that I shall now proceed to apply my analysis to the relationship between man's responsible choices and the lower levels of reality in which man's existence is founded.

Remember the relation of machines to the nature of the materials of which they are made. I have gone into this in detail for I hoped that it might throw light on the subject now before us; let me try to show that it does. The operational principles of a machine would guarantee invariable success to it, but for the fact that they can go into action only if embodied in tangible materials which carry in them always the possibility of failure. Human responsibility too is subject to a similar intrinsic limitation; it can operate only if embodied in human beings who are liable to failure. For no responsibility is taken where no hazard is to be met, and a hazard is a liability to failure. Moreover, while men are by nature subject to lust, pain and pride, which makes them liable to dereliction of duty, these self-centred drives are indispensable elements of a responsible commitment. For only by staking our lower interests can we bear witness effectively to our higher purposes. Lastly, in all our mental achievements we rely ultimately on the machinery of our body, and this limits the scope and endangers the proper functions of our faculties. A breakdown of this machine may even affect directly man's capacity for responsible choices, by rendering him pathologically feckless, apathetic or obsessed. *Everywhere the potential operations of a higher level are actualized by their embodiment in lower levels which makes them liable to failure.*

We can extend this principle to the social relations of responsible choices. The human mind exists only within an articulate framework provided for it by society; society both fosters thought and is in its turn largely controlled by thought. Hence the responsibility for every major mental decision is in part a social responsibility, and thus both affects and is in turn affected, by the existing structure of power and profit. I shall speak of these inter-relations in my next lecture; but we can anticipate here their bearing on our present subject. In an ideal free society each person would have perfect access to the truth: to the truth in science, in art, religion and justice, both in public and private life. But this is not practicable; each person can know directly very little of truth and must trust others for the rest. Indeed, to assure this process of mutual reliance is one of the main functions of society. It follows that such freedom of the mind as can be possessed by men is due to the services of social institutions, which set narrow limits to man's freedom and tend to threaten it even within these limits. The relation is analogous to that between mind and body: to the way in which the performance of mental acts is restricted by limitations and distortions due to the medium which makes these performances possible.

What then is our answer to those who would doubt that man made of matter, man driven by appetites and subject to social commands, can sustain purely mental purposes? The answer is that he can. He can do this under his own responsibility, precisely by submitting to restrictive and stultifying circumstances which lie beyond his responsibility. These circumstances offer us opportunities for pure thought—limited opportunities and full of pitfalls—but all the same, they *are* opportunities, and they are ours: *we* are responsible for using or neglecting them.

*   *   *

Viewed in the cosmic perspective of space and time, the opportunity for engaging on works of the mind may have a special appeal to us. For so far as we know, we on this earth are the only bearers of thought in the universe. Nor has this gift been a feature of terrestrial life from the start. Five million centuries of evolution, groping upwards along numberless paths, have led to this result only in us, in us human beings. And ours has as yet been a brief venture. After five million centuries of evolution, we have been engaged only for fifty centuries in a literate process of thought. It has all been the affair of the last hundred generations or so.

This task, therefore, appears to be the particular calling of literate man in this universe. This is the perspective in which I want you to consider all that I have said so far, and what I yet propose to say later.

If this perspective is true, a supreme trust is placed in us by the whole creation, and it is sacrilege then even to contemplate actions which may lead to the extinction of humanity. Nothing can then justify such actions in any circumstances. I believe that no one who thankfully acknowledges man's calling in this universe, be he religious or agnostic, can avoid this ultimate peremptory conclusion.

LECTURE THREE

Understanding History

W^{E HAVE} seen that by accrediting knowledge gained through understanding we obtain an insight into the stratification of reality, and that human thought represents the highest level of reality in our experience. The true nature of a thing composed of different levels of reality was found revealed by its most comprehensive feature, forming its uppermost level. This feature must be recognized first, before we can appreciate the subsidiary role played in respect of it by the particulars forming the lower levels. It follows then that the study of man must start with an appreciation of man in the act of making responsible decisions.

The most striking examples of human decisions are recorded by history. They are the acts of the men whom Hegel called 'world historical personalities', men like Alexander, Augustus, Charlemagne, Luther

Cromwell, Napoleon, Bismarck, Hitler, Lenin. Pioneers in science and philosophy, great poets, painters and composers, the heroes of moral or religious martyrdom, may have served nobler aims and have been, in the long run, more influential. But it is political actions profoundly affecting the framework of existing power, that form the most striking human choices. It is these which make up the drama of history and these which have been the main subject-matter of historians telling a dramatic story of past ages.

Since the end of the nineteenth century there has been a continuous philosophic movement on foot claiming that the humanities, and history in particular, must be studied by other methods than those of the natural sciences. In Germany, where this movement goes back to Hegel and Herder, and in Italy, where its roots can be traced even further to Vico, this philosophic movement soon became predominant. In England, the writings of Collingwood, who vigorously advocated what he called the 'secession' of history from the domain of the natural sciences, gained a limited influence for this doctrine.

The position at which I have arrived in the previous two lectures denies any discontinuity between the study of nature and the study of man. It claims that all knowledge rests on understanding, and that in this sense knowledge is of the same kind at all levels of existence. But this position admits, at the same time, that as the subject of our understanding ascends to higher levels of existence, it reveals ever new comprehensive features, the study of which requires ever new powers of understanding. I shall readily acknowledge, accordingly, that historians must exercise a special kind of understanding. But I shall argue also that all the distinctive characteristics of the historian's method emerge by continuous stages from the progressive modification of the methods used within science. As the scientist gradually advances from the study of inanimate nature to that of life, approaching first lower, then higher forms of life and eventually ascending to the study of intelligence in the higher animals, ever higher modes of comprehension come into play, and the study of man merely adds to these yet one more, still higher mode of comprehension. The characteristic features of historiography will thus be shown to emerge by the continuation of a development broadly prefigured already within the natural sciences.

I shall begin by surveying the rising stages of comprehension within science, up to the threshold of the humanities, and show how comprehension becomes here progressively more intense and more complex. Look first at the theories of physics. They deal with the ultimate particulars of nature and establish the existence of patterns, formed by them in space and time. Passionate intimations of this harmonious order are the guides of discovery in physics, and the beauty of a physical theory is the mark of its scientific value. This beauty is enjoyed by dwelling in the theory and observing its confirmation by the facts; the physicist dwells with pleasure in the patterns of inanimate nature, while he turns away coldly from disorderly, meaningless collocations of particles.

These structural elements of understanding are much reinforced and enriched at the next level, described in the previous lecture, on which we shall now group together machines, tools, etc., with living beings situated on the vegetative level of existence. We have found that new, more striking, forms of excellence and failure emerge here, and that the participation of a person understanding such things is thereby intensified. We recognized that to know a machine is to enter into its purpose and acknowledge the rationality of its operations and that to know an organism is to acknowledge the existence of an individual and appreciate its correct growth, form and function, these features being judged to be healthy or abnormal by standards which we consider apposite to an individual as a member of its species.

This intensification of meaning and understanding was seen to form a consistent trend as we moved on to the deliberate activities of animals. The individual's responses are here no longer restricted to adjusting himself to his environment; they are striving to control it. The animal, bent on satisfying its appetites, seeks to know what is confronting it. In doing so, it forms expectations which may be correct or mistaken. Rightness and failure of this kind can both occur in a healthy individual and they are additional, therefore, to the alternatives of health and disease, to which all living beings are liable on the vegetative level. I will lend greater precision to this distinction now by outlining it in terms of its logical structure.

Let me show first that while the observation of vegetative life takes place, like that of an inanimate body, on only two logical levels, observations of a deliberately active animal will in general involve three logical levels. The device of logical levels can be exemplified as follows. When I say 'the stone is rolling' this involves two logical levels, (1) one for me and my statement about the stone, and (2) another for the stone itself. Usually we think of ourselves on the higher level, talking down to the stone on the lower level. But if I say 'the sentence "the stone is rolling" is true', I need an additional, third, level to accommodate the three things brought together by this utterance. There will be (1) a topmost level for myself and my utterance, (2) an intermediate level for the sentence of which I am saying that it is true, and (3) a bottom level, once more, for the stone.

Statements about living beings that are merely vegetating are like statements about stones; they involve only two logical levels. But when an animal starts doing and knowing things, it ascends to a logical level situated above the level of the things that it is trying to control. Here is an illustration. When I say 'the cat is alive', this involves only two levels, just like 'the stone is rolling'; but when I say 'the cat sees a rat' this involves three levels. The uppermost for me, the middle one for the cat and the lowest for the rat. This logical structure allows us to say of an animal's perception that it is true or mistaken, which we cannot say of its breathing or digestion. And this brings with it a fundamental enrichment of our understanding. For when we think that an animal is capable of error, we also attribute to it a measure of conscious judgment. The more complex, three-levelled, logical structure is thus accompanied by an expansion of our fellow feeling which makes us aware of the animal's sentience.

To acknowledge the capacity for judgment and error in an animal, is to recognize in it also an interpretative framework which we may deem right or wrong from the animal's point of view, and this leads to a distinction between two kinds of mistakes. Trout, snapping at the angler's fly, are making an error based on an otherwise correct interpretation of experience. On the other hand, when young geese, having accepted a human being as their mother, go on identifying other humans in the same mistaken manner, they are judging their experience correctly in relation to an erroneous interpretative framework. Both kinds of failure can be distinguished from a pathological absence of judgment, as observed e.g. in rats deprived of a major portion of their brain. Add to these three types of failure the case of correct judgment, and we have a fourfold classification of deliberate choices, which will be seen to prefigure a similar grading of decisions made by the historian.

But before crossing the gap between the intelligence of animals and the thoughts of man, let us narrow the separation of the two yet a little further. We can do so by acknowledging the presence of intellectual passions on a rudimentary level in some animals. There is evidence (already mentioned in passing) to show that higher animals can be worried by a problem in a way not accounted for by the mere failure to obtain an expected reward. They can be harassed by some problems to the point of suffering a nervous breakdown, and they are found correspondingly to enjoy an ingenious solution as a game, merely for its intellectual beauty. We have here the incipient transcendence of self-centred individuality by a personhood striving to achieve intellectual excellence for its own sake.

I shall now proceed from the natural sciences to the humanities and shall face up in doing so to the contrasts between the writing of history and the study of nature on the grounds on which philosophers have claimed to distinguish the methods and domains of these two forms of knowledge. Keeping in mind that of all historic studies it is dramatic history that represents the most intimate approach to the responsible decisions of man, let us take Napoleon's career to exemplify the subject-matter of history and let us contrast it with universal gravitation, the mathematical theory of which may be said to approximate most closely the ideal of a completely abstract scientific knowledge.

Napoleon's career forms a series of *actions*, while gravitation comprises merely *events*, not actions. Human action involves responsibility, which raises the question of motive: such questions, for example, as how far Napoleon was responsible for the wars waged by France under his leadership. Professor Pieter Geyl has compared the views of twenty-seven French historians of Napoleon on these and similar questions. He gave his survey the title *Napoleon For and Against*, which shows that the historians' analysis of motives has resulted in the apportioning of *praise* and *blame*. Such matters are absent in the physicist's approach to his subject-matter. Since this matter comprises no actions, no questions of moral responsibility can arise in respect of it. This contrast is deepened by the fact that in order to appreciate Napoleon's motives you must put yourself in his position and re-live his thoughts, and that, quite naturally, the result of such indwelling will depend to some extent on the person who enters on the indwelling. Professor Geyl observes, accordingly, that the appreciation of Napoleon depends on the political views of the historian. He finds that these views have varied with the date of writing and the professional affiliations of the historian. Feelings of national pride or anti-clericalism favour Napoleon, while anti-militarism and religious feelings speak against him. We may recall how our own reactions to the Russian Revolution have recently caused historians to work out new interpretations of the French Revolution and of the Millenarian movements that preceded it. Thus, the writing of history is itself a process of history and this seems to distinguish it sharply from physics, chemistry or biology.

I shall take each of these points in turn as I have just listed them. The contrast between actions recorded by history and events studied by natural science vanishes altogether if we recall that animal psychology, which deals with the actions of animals, lies within the domain of natural science. It is true that only human actions are subject to moral judgment. But, contrary to

usually accepted opinion, every branch of natural
science makes value judgments of some kind. Each
appreciates the particular comprehensive entities which
form its own subject-matter, and the corresponding
standards of excellence form an ascending series continuously progressing towards a moral valuation of
human actions. The physicist sets standards of perfection to the patterns of inanimate matter and the
naturalist sets them for the shapes of different plants
and animals; the physiologist establishes for each
species a set of standards which define the healthy
functions of its organs, its proper appetites and right
perception; and lastly the animal psychologist assigns
to individual animals the kinds of problems which will
match their mental powers and assesses their ingenuity by their responses to these problems. These
valuations become more penetrating and more complex at every successive stage.

They also become progressively more intimate, and
this links up with another relation of natural science to
history. It recalls that no knowledge of nature lacks
some measure of indwelling of the observer in his
subject-matter, and that the intimacy of this indwelling
shows a continuous progression towards that fullest
indwelling which has been rightly claimed to be a
characteristic method of the historian. The physicist
may dwell deeply in a mathematical theory, but he en-

joys above all its general qualities: its grandeur, simplicity and accuracy. The chemist shows already a somewhat different affinity to his subject. He finds pleasure in the peculiarities of compounds and the delicately graded conditions of chemical changes. The naturalist's love of living shapes and vital functions is even more intimate. The identification of specimens of a known species involves a much higher degree of connoisseurship than the identification of a specimen of a known chemical substance. And as we rise to the study of animal behaviour we enter into a whole universe of sensations, appetites and purposive activities which we understand only by deeply identifying ourselves with the animal. Rising even higher, we establish contact with the animal's intelligence, and this indwelling is so intimate that we can learn to set problems to it which will evoke its most intense mental efforts and so bring it to the verge of mental breakdown. It seems hardly extravagant to extrapolate from here to the further step which will make us understand an historic figure like Napoleon by re-living his personal problems.

We cannot, therefore, distinguish history from the natural sciences on any of the first three grounds that have been so far suggested, namely (1) that the historian studies actions rather than mere events, and (2) that he evaluates these actions according to standards that he regards proper to them, and (3) that he does so by re-living the actions of his subject.

But can we also match the variations of standards applied to Napoleon according to the personal affiliations of historians, by any even remotely analogous variations in the interpretative framework of biologists or animal psychologists?

The politically grounded orthodoxies imposed on these branches of science in the Soviet Union seem to demonstrate that political influence can only corrupt science. But this question requires a wider setting. Remember the way in which we built up the conception of human responsibility by demonstrating how successive levels of rightness can operate only within subsidiary particulars that inevitably restrict and often stultify its operations. This conception of a stratified universe which cannot be defined in terms of its particulars was shown to be a necessary foundation for a conception of man serving the truth; and the acceptance of this conception was deemed in its turn to be the foundation of a free society. Clearly, if this logical sequence is correct, my love of a free society, which tacitly affirms its reality, also testifies to the stratified structure of the universe as its logically necessary antecedent. And why not? We have shown that every act of understanding somewhat rectifies our being, and may well accept therefore also that a conversion to a truer way of *being a man* will induce a better *under-standing of man.* To this extent I subscribe to Marx's thesis that the social being of man determines man's consciousness—though I reject altogether the economic determinism implied in his formula.

But we have yet to deal with the distinctive feature claimed for history in Windelband's rectorial allocution of 1894 which first effectively declared the secession of history from the natural sciences. He contrasted the *uniqueness* of historic events with the *repetitiveness* of the events studied by the natural sciences. This distinction was actually claimed to be sharp only in the sense of representing two logically distinct approaches, the theoretical and the factual, both of which were present in every kind of knowledge. The distinctive position of history was thought to be due to the predominance of the factual interest over the theoretical, as compared with the natural sciences, for which the reverse was true. Hence a continuously graded sequence of sciences, with variable proportions of unique to generalized features, was seen to lead from mathematical physics to the study of history. But no attempt was made to explain why the ratio of the two logically disparate components should vary in this manner.

Windelband's brief observations have been systematically enlarged upon by Rickert. For my part, I

would re-state the relation between uniqueness and
repetitiveness in the various sciences in my own terms
as follows. In my view, the pursuit of science is motivated throughout by a passion to understand; and, in a
more general sense, the craving to understand actuates
the whole mental life of man. This craving is satisfied
most fully when it grasps an idea which promises yet to
reveal large, still unfathomable, implications. Anything
so deep-seated will appear profoundly real and will
excite a passionate interest. This applies in several
different ways to all human thought, and it applies
differently even to different branches of the natural
sciences. Physics achieves profundity by its immense
accurate generalizations, despite its otherwise shallow
inanimate subject-matter. The fragmentary and im-
precise insights of biology give equal satisfaction, because their lesser generality and accuracy is compen-
sated for by the intrinsic profundity of living beings.
The next move in this direction takes us from biology
to dramatic history. The depth of a Napoleon's per-
sonality is such that it requires great works of history
for its interpretation and such works are of sufficient
interest without offering broad generalizations. But if
no great men had lived, no dramatic history could be
written. Accounts of the past would then be either re-
duced to intellectually valueless chronicles. or else be
limited to the analysis of general political economic and

social changes. This theoretical approach to history can achieve merit, for its less interesting particulars offer scope for a wider sweep of the mind.

To sum up. Every pebble is unique, but profoundly unique objects are rare. Wherever these are found (whether in nature or among the members of human society) they are interesting in themselves. They offer opportunity for intimate indwelling and for a systematic study of their individuality. Since great men are more profoundly unique than any object in nature, they sustain a far more elaborate study of uniqueness than any natural object can. Hence the peculiar position of dramatic history at the end of a row of sciences of increasing intimacy and delicate complexity, yet offset against all of them by an exceptionally vigorous and subtle participation in its subject-matter.

A theory of knowledge which regards the study of history as akin to the natural sciences and acknowledges the fact that history refers to a distinctive level of reality, neither accepts nor rejects the 'secession' of history from the domain of science. It leaves us instead with the task of defining as closely as possible within this theory of knowledge the situation of the human mind, when engaged in the study of human actions recorded by history. These ultimate steps in our enquiry into the study of man will be taken by resuming an earlier line of thought.

I have said before that man is the only creature in the world to whom we owe respect. This appreciation differs from that accorded to the harmonies of the inanimate world or to the excellence of lower forms of life, by referring to things that are purely of the mind. These things, noble actions, works of art or science, serve no material need, but demand, on the contrary, material sacrifices: they are deemed excellent in themselves. And it is because man is capable of such sacrifice that he himself demands to be respected, and will be respected by those who share his respect for the things to which his sacrifices bear witness. We have seen that this is the spiritual foundation of freedom and of mutual respect among men. And this is also the framework, therefore, within which man *writing* history confronts the men who *made* history.

Any claim to respect awarded on such grounds, admits a liability to reproach on the same grounds. This liability is qualified owing to the limitations imposed on men's mental passions by the medium through which they operate; I mean the medium of bodily existence and social dependence which lies beyond man's responsibility and thereby defines his calling. This material and social rootedness affects the mental life of man by three types of shortcomings which I have prefigured when classifying the failures of the self-centred intelligence of animals. They are:

86

(1) faults committed within an acceptable framework;
(2) rational applications of an unacceptable framework; (3) pathological actions, not subject to human responsibility. These three types of criticism will be now shown to offer occasion for three fallacies in evaluating historical actions.

Historians are concerned predominantly with the moral and political greatness or shortcomings of historic personages, and they have to exercise their own moral and political judgment in respect of these subjects within the same type of limitations for which they have to allow in their subjects. The limitations imposed on the historian by his local rootedness are ineradicable, since any attempt to eradicate them would also have to operate *within* these limitations. The extent to which each of us accepts and relies on the existing medium of society for shaping his own thoughts and aspirations is therefore an ultimate tacit commitment of ours. I acknowledge this commitment myself as the framework of declaring myself thus committed. This is, indeed, merely to accept for myself the situation which I have defined as the calling of man.

Viewed in this light we can see the possibility of three types of historical fallacies connected with the three ways of criticizing historical actions. (1) History may be written by applying our own standards, without allowing for the difference in the historical setting of the acting persons. Historians of the eighteenth century, like Voltaire and Gibbon, tended to judge the past in this narrow-minded manner. We may call this the rationalist fallacy. (2) The rise of the historical method known as historicism has transformed our conception of history by striving to judge past actions by the standards of their own time. This method, when taken to its limit, would sanction absolute conformity and render thereby any criticism of the standards of a time meaningless. It fosters an extreme, altogether fallacious, relativism. (3) The reduction of man's moral scope is taken a step further by a materialist conception of history in which all actions appear determined by impulses of power and profit. Interpreted on these lines, all actions are devoid of moral meaning, and man is deprived altogether of responsibility to ideal obligations. This is the determinist fallacy.

The rationalist fallacy arises from applying a criticism of type 1 without regard for the limitations imposed on a person's responsibility by the acceptance of his native intellectual framework. The relativist fallacy is due to the opposite error: it arises by applying criticism of type 2 while entirely ignoring the person's responsibility for accepting the framework in which he is brought up. The determinist fallacy arises by applying to sane subjects a criticism of type 3 which presupposes the insanity of the subject.

A balanced respect for man avoids all three fallacies. It acknowledges that it is man's task to strive by the aid of his meagre creaturely faculties and of the resources of his particular environment to achieve results not altogether determined by these opportunities. In this light the historian will see every historical person as necessarily dependent for his effectiveness on accepting a given cultural medium and on grasping accidental opportunities that are never free of degrading temptations. But he will yet see each person deciding for himself how much of the surrounding culture to accept as given and making up his own mind what opportunities to take or to miss, what temptations to resist or succumb to. Never will the historian admit that such circumstances can irresistibly determine a sane man's deliberate actions. He will avoid then all three fallacies as follows: (1) the rationalist fallacy—by admitting the indispensable biological and cultural rootedness of all free actions; (2) the relativist fallacy—by acknowledging that each man has some measure of direct access to the standards of truth and rightness and must limit for their sake at some point his subjection to given circumstances, and (3) the determinist fallacy—by committing himself to a personal knowledge of the human mind as a seat of responsible choices.

This completes the parallelism between the social

rootedness of man's responsible judgment and the rootedness of the animal's deliberate appetitive decisions in the mechanism of its reflexes and lower bodily functions. We can now extend this argument to deal with yet another ground on which philosophers of history have claimed the secession of historiography from the natural sciences.

Man's responsibility to standards of truth and rightness establishes him as a rational person, capable of doing mathematics, administering justice, writing poetry, and performing other purely mental actions. Therefore, in so far as human history consists of such actions, the historian can understand what men of the past have done, in the same sense in which we can understand a mathematical proof or the judicial decisions of a court of law. Rational conclusions or actions can be justified in terms of their reasons, and to this extent a rational decision remains valid anywhere and for all times, irrespective of the circumstances in which it was actually first arrived at in the course of past history. It is argued therefore that by understanding such a decision the historian grasps an eternal, immaterial subject that, as such, lies outside the domain of the natural sciences.

This claim is supplemented by contrasting rational human actions with a pathological behaviour caused, e.g., by a brain injury. Since such diseased behaviour is quite unreasonable, it cannot be understood at all in terms of reasons; but it can be understood instead in terms of its causes, which are a fit subject-matter only for the natural sciences. Though the pathological behaviour of a Tiberius or a Hitler may be a matter of historical record, it lies outside the historian's distinctive task which is to understand the responsible decisions of historic personages.

I agree to this distinction; it is both clear and important. But I would add that we have come across the same distinction already in more general terms and found it to apply between different branches of knowledge within the natural sciences. It is the distinction between a comprehensive principle operating at a higher level and the effects of the particulars belonging to a lower level on which these operations must rely. I shall show this by reformulating this distinction once more in terms of rational *versus* causal explanations and extending it at the same time to cover the whole range of this enquiry.

A correct judicial decision is an action that can be explained by its reasons, but it is also the action of the judge as a creature of flesh and blood. Insofar as the judge is acting in the service of justice, his mind and body function subsidiarily to the process of justice. This process must rely on the judge's mental powers, such as his memory and imagination, and on his bodily functions, such as his proper feeding and healthy digestion, and these in their turn will rely on the laws governing the physical and chemical processes which subsidiarily constitute them. But there are limits to the extent to which the effects of particulars will subserve a comprehensive operation, and beyond these limits they will cause it to miscarry. Both the memory and imagination of a judge may mislead him; his healthy bodily desires may impair his legal judgment; and the natural processes of physics and chemistry may destroy his health. Consequently, although the sciences of psychology, physiology, physics and chemistry cannot account for a correct judicial decision, they may account (at least in principle) for miscarriages of justice. The causes of such errors may be psychological, physiological, and in the last resort, bio-chemical or bio-physical.

But consider now the system of appetites in itself. While the bodily appetites of a judge may impair the rationality of his decisions, viewed in themselves these appetites and physiological functions form a rational system. The process of taking food, of seeking shelter, of amassing wealth, can be accounted for by adequate reasons; and, at the same time, this lower level of rationality is once more threatened by causes issuing from a still lower level. The particulars which normally subserve the rational functioning of self-centred appetites, may disturb its functions by causing diseases and errors.

Rationality prevails again throughout the stratagems of life that take place on the lower, vegetative level. We say that the *reason* for the presence of the cardial valves is to keep the blood flowing round, while we regard defects of these valves as *causes* of circulatory troubles.

This analysis both confirms the autonomy of historiography—and of other disciplines whose primary concern is to elucidate their subject-matter in terms of reasons—and shows at the same time, (1) that the natural sciences also include such branches of knowledge, and (2) that studies of rationality remain always rooted in an ancillary knowledge of causes operating on lower levels of reality. I shall now try to elucidate more fully both this continuity and this disparity between historiography and biology, by showing how the characteristic encounter of an historian with an historical personage is continuous with the relation between the biologist and his living object.

Remember that the observation of an inanimate body takes place on two logical levels—the higher one for the observer, the lower one for the object—and that the same is still true for the observation of living beings at the vegetative level. Remember how a third level comes into being, when we observe an animal which is itself an observer—the highest level being then used for the biologist, the middle one for the animal, and the lowest for the things the animal observes. We shall take into account now that this clean separation of logical levels is hampered everywhere by the structure of personal knowledge. For all clues, signs, tools and any other particulars of which the observer is subsidiarily aware may be said to be assimilated to himself, and belong in this sense to the logical level on which the observer himself is placed, while the same things form also part of the object situated on the lower level below that of the observer. All these things are, therefore, subsidiarily placed on one level and focally on another level, which impairs the separation of the two levels.

Now take into account also that the participation of the knower in the thing he knows increases steadily as the objects of knowledge ascend to ever higher levels of existence, and that, correspondingly, the observer also applies ever higher standards of appreciation to the things known by him. These two trends will combine to an ever more ample and also more equal sharing of existence between the knower and the known, so that when we reach the point at which one man knows another man, the knower so fully dwells in that which he knows, that we can no longer place the two on different logical levels. This is to say that when we arrive at the contemplation of a human being as a responsible person, and we apply to him the same standards as we accept for ourselves, our knowledge of him has definitely lost the character of an observation and has become an encounter instead.

Nor is this yet the end of this progression. Let me pass on to its final stage and illustrate it in the first place in terms of historiography. Dramatic history is written about prominent historical personages who are usually controversial figures. Historians—whether hostile or friendly—must apply to such personages standards of historical responsibility that are not derived from their own experience in life. Take more particularly the admirers of a great historical figure, such as Napoleon. An admiring historian studies Napoleon as his disciple. He participates, in fact, in a cult, the emotional streams of which have filled people throughout Europe for over a century. Napoleon's figure has served as an ideal of ruthless greatness in Continental literature and philosophy ever since his day. Stendhal's Julien Sorel, Balzac's Rastignac, Pushkin's Herrman (in the *Queen of Spades*), Dostoievsky's Raskolnikoff—they are so many portraits of the Napoleon-struck youths of France and Russia. In Germany the movement culminated in the popular influence of Nietzsche, who describes Napoleon in the *Genealogy of Morals* as the embodiment of the noble ideal uniting the brutish

95

with the more than human. From Nietzsche the cult passed on to our own days, right down to the frown of Mussolini and the forelock of Hitler.

To contemplate a person as an ideal is to submit to his authority. The admirer of Napoleon does not judge him by independent previously established standards, but accepts, on the contrary, the figure of Napoleon as a standard for judging himself. Such an admirer may be mistaken in the choice of his hero, but his relation to greatness is correct. We need reverence to perceive greatness, even as we need a telescope to observe spiral nebulae.

But let me widen my argument here so as to comprise its purpose more fully, I promised at the start of these lectures that by accepting understanding as a means of establishing knowledge we would achieve a continuity of knowledge extending from the natural sciences to the humanities. I fulfilled this promise up to a point by displaying a succession of comprehensive levels in the manner of Chinese boxes, with the purely mental life of man embracing all the others. This last, I said, was man's distinctive form of existence, evoked by his intellectual passions from the soil of a cultural heritage: a life of thought, bent on the search for truth and other manners of excellence akin to truth. I observed that his access to truth and to all other human ideals was the ground on which man claimed freedom and respect, and on which he actually received both freedom and respect from those who respected the same grounds. Such indeed, I concluded, were the spiritual foundations of a free society, the achievement of which was man's cosmic calling.

We are now being led back to these ultimate matters by our examination of historiography in its relation to the natural sciences. A reverent submission to greatness has been found to form the ultimate member of a series of studies applied to an ascending sequence of realities. Starting from physics, we passed through the rising levels of biological sciences and arrived at the study of man as the agent of responsible choices; and then, when from this encounter of equals we went on to the study of heroes, we found ourselves paying homage to our subject and educating ourselves in its image. Clearly, when arrived here, we can no longer think of ourselves as observers occupying, as such, a logical level above that of our object. If we can still distinguish two levels we are now looking *up* to our object, not down.

I have purposely chosen as my example the figure of Napoleon to remind us that this process of education may amount to a corruption. This should show how we both submissively depend for our whole universe of thought on the masters whose deeds and works we reverently study, and yet how independent we are, and indeed how hazardously self-reliant, in accepting them as our masters. This choice must indeed ultimately fall back on us, since no authority can teach us how to choose between itself and its rivals. We must enter here on an ultimate commitment which coincides essentially with the act of deciding to what extent we should accept as given the social and mental milieu within which we shall deploy our own thoughts and feelings. By recognizing our heroes and masters we accept our particular calling.

At this point the study of man is definitively transformed into a process of self-education. Instead of observing an object, or even encountering a person, we are now apprenticing ourselves to the understanding and imitation of the great minds of the past. We are dedicating ourselves to the service of obligations for which they have legislated. We are entering on a framework of expressions and standards by the guidance of which our minds will be enlarged and disciplined.

At the end of my first lecture I gave the study of pure mathematics and the intelligent enjoyment of music as examples of an indwelling of this kind, and said that the whole universe of human sensibilities—of intellectual, moral, artistic, religious ideas—was evoked by living and growing up within the framework of our cultural heritage. I said that this process was moved by a passionate craving to understand,

which causes our mind to unfold into forms of existence more satisfying to its transmuted self. We have
now arrived once more, by extrapolating the series of
studies which led from physics to historiography, at
the point where our possession of knowledge is seen to
consist in an act of understanding and submission.

*　　*　　*

And this leads on without a break to my own situation here as I address this University College founded
by Lord Lindsay. Much has been heard in the past
twenty years of the duties which universities owe to
society, and of course, universities must train doctors
and technicians and other specialists useful to the
community. But these obligations are trivial when
compared with the claims which universities have on
society. For the universities form an eminent part of
the framework which shapes the mind of modern man.
University teachers are today the chief transmitters
and interpreters of the heritage which defines the duties
of men and sets up the standards that society must respect. The principal obligation of universities is to
teach young people, and among them our future
leaders, the basic truths to the service of which a free
society is dedicated.

I believe that this conception of a university in
society may claim close kinship with that embodied by
Lord Lindsay in this University College.

99

Bibliographical Note

THE movement towards a secession of history from the domain of the natural sciences which forms the subject of the Third Lecture is surveyed by Collingwood in his posthumous book, *The Idea of History*. This book is so popular (and rightly popular) among English students that it seems necessary to mention certain points in which I differ from Collingwood in the evaluation of the works of Windelband, Rickert and Dilthey, named by him as the founders of the modern 'anti-positivist' movement in the theory of historical knowledge.

Collingwood's sharp criticism of Windelband's rectorial address delivered at Strasburg in 1894 is based on a misrepresentation. Windelband does not say that the field of reality can be divided into the subjects of nomothetic and idiographic knowledge. He expressly denies this and asserts that these two forms of knowledge are two logically distinct parts of all knowledge.

Nor is Windelband 'strangely blind' to the objections raised by Schopenhauer against the scientific character of history on the grounds that history deals with unique events. Windelband refers to Schopenhauer on the very same lines as Collingwood does in criticizing him. This explains certain differences in my own references to Windelband compared with Collingwood's account of his views. I must also point out that Collingwood describes Rickert's views inaccurately. In his great work, *Die Grenzen der naturwissenschaftlichen Begriffsbildung* (1902) Rickert does *not* say that the valuation of historical acts is a proper function of historiography. He says on the contrary, and argues it in detail, that history *as a science* can merely identify acts deserving praise or blame, while strictly refraining from apportioning either praise or blame. In the later editions of his book (1921 and 1929) he upholds this view first against Troeltsch and then also against Meinecke, who had meanwhile taken their stand on the doctrine that historical interpretation includes moral valuation. By contrast, Rickert acknowledges Max Weber as a follower of his own doctrine of value-free science. My own text refers therefore to Troeltsch, Meinecke and Collingwood, rather than to Rickert and Max Weber.

Finally, a word about Dilthey, whom Collingwood places above Windelband and Rickert among the first 'secessionists'. Dilthey has since been richly interpreted for English readers by Hodges. His work forms part of a great intellectual network which includes phenomenology and existentialism and has transformed the whole climate of philosophy on the Continent of Europe. Out of it has issued modern Gestalt psychology, which I myself am trying to restore to its function as a theory of knowledge adumbrated in its philosophical origins. Many of my statements are reminiscent of this movement; but let me recall that its thought was based throughout on the exclusion of the natural sciences from its scope.

PHOENIX BOOKS
in Philosophy

PHOENIX BOOKS
in Science

PHOENIX SCIENCE SERIES

PHOENIX BOOKS
in Sociology

PHOENIX BOOKS
in Political Science